CELLO

TEAM STRINGS

CHRISTOPHER BULL
OLIVE GOODBORN &
RICHARD DUCKETT

International Music Publications Limited

Edited by BARRIE CARSON TURNER

Piano accompaniments by CHRISTOPHER BULL

INTERNATIONAL MUSIC PUBLICATIONS LIMITED would like to thank the following publishers for permission to use arrangements
of their copyright material in TEAM STRINGS.
LITTLE DONKEY - Words and Music by ERIC BOSWELL
© 1959 & 1993 Chappell Music Ltd., London W1Y 3FA
CONGRATULATIONS - Words and Music by BILL MARTIN and PHIL COULTER
© 1968 & 1993 Peter Maurice Music Co. Ltd., London WC2H 0EA
EDELWEISS (From THE SOUND OF MUSIC) - Lyrics by
OSCAR HAMMERSTEIN II, Music by RICHARD RODGERS
© 1959 Richard Rodgers and Oscar Hammerstein II
Copyright renewed
This arrangement © 1993 Williamson Music Co., owner of publication and allied rights throughout the World.
PALOMA BLANCA - Words and Music by J BOUWENS
© 1975 & 1993 Witch/Veronic Music, Holland
Noon Music Ltd., London W1Y 3FA
SING A RAINBOW - Words and Music by ARTHUR HAMILTON
© 1955 & 1993 Mark vii Ltd. and WB Music Corp., USA
Warner Chappell Music Ltd., London W1Y 3FA
THE WHITE CLIFFS OF DOVER - Words by WALTER KENT, Music by NAT BURTON
© 1941 & 1993 Shapiro Bernstein & Co. Inc., USA
B. Feldman & Co., Ltd., London WC2H 0EA
LOVE ME TENDER - Words and Music by VERA MATSON and ELVIS PRESLEY
© 1956 & 1993 Elvis Presley Music Inc., USA
Carlin Music Corp., London NW1 8BD
HAPPY BIRTHDAY TO YOU - Words and Music by PATTY S HILL and MILDRED HILL
© 1935 (renewed 1962) & 1993 Summy-Birchard Music (a division of Summy-Birchard Inc.), USA
Keith Prowse Music Pub. Co. Ltd., London WC2H 0EA
CHITTY CHITTY BANG BANG - Words and Music by RICHARD SHERMAN and ROBERT SHERMAN
© 1967 & 1993 EMI Catalogue Partnership/EMI Unart Catalog Inc., USA
EMI United Partnership Ltd., London WC2H 0EA
BLOWIN' IN THE WIND - Words and Music by BOB DYLAN
© 1963 & 1993 Witmark & Sons, USA
Warner Chappell Music Ltd., London W1Y 3FA

Sincere thanks are extended to the following people:
ANN GOODBORN, Double Bass Tutor, Birmingham Schools Symphony Orchestra, for her invaluable advice on technical matters.
ANGELA GREGORY of Kings Norton Girls School, Birmingham, and all the pupils who worked on the material in preparation.

First Published 1993.
© International Music Publications Limited, Griffin House, 161 Hammersmith Road, London W6 8BS, England.
Cover Design: IAN BARRETT
Cover Photography: RON GOLDBY
Production: STEPHEN CLARK and MARK MUMFORD
Typesetting: Headline Publicity Ltd., Chelmsford, Essex
Instruments photographed are "Andreas Zeller" courtesy of Stentor Music Co. Ltd., Reigate, England.
Printed in England

TEAM STRINGS: Cello
Book only: Order ref.18417:   ISBN 1-84328-639-4.
Book & CD: Order ref. 6776A: ISBN 1-84328-664-5.

Team Strings Ensemble

TEAM STRINGS ensemble material has been specially written so that it can be played by almost any combination of string instruments the teacher may encounter.

On each ensemble page there are three parts. The first is the melody and the second is a duet part. The third is either a bass line, a harmony part or a descant. Each piece can therefore be used as a solo, duet, or trio, with or without piano accompaniment.

By allocating the parts to different instruments it is easy to create a considerable variety of mixed ensembles, from a simple duet to a full string orchestra.

In addition to this, each piece can be extended into a longer one by varying the textures in subsequent verses. This can be done by reallocating the parts, playing in unison, using *pizzicato* accompaniments, introducing solo passages, etc.

The following symbols have been used to provide an immediate visual identification:

 Pieces with piano accompaniment

 Ensemble page
(score included in ACCOMPANIMENTS book)

☐ Pieces which appear in the same place on the same page in all four TEAM STRINGS books.

Introducing Team Strings

The TEAM STRINGS series has been designed to meet the needs of young string players everywhere, whether lessons are given individually, in groups or in the classroom.

Musical variety

Each book contains a wide variety of musical styles, from the Baroque and Classical eras to Christmas carols, folk music, and popular favourites. In addition there are many original pieces, studies and technical exercises. Furthermore, TEAM STRINGS offers material for mixed string ensemble as well as solos with piano accompaniment.

Ensemble pieces

All TEAM STRINGS books contain corresponding pages of music which can be played together in harmony. Thus, even beginners are given early ensemble experience and the opportunity to share lessons with other players.

Every TEAM STRINGS book contains a supplement relating to the duets in TEAM WOODWIND for flute and oboe. There are also string parts which can be used in conjunction with TEAM BRASS, TEAM WOODWIND and TEAM PERCUSSION to form mixed instrumental ensembles.

National Curriculum & GCSE skills

TEAM STRINGS has been designed to help meet the requirements of the National Curriculum for music. In addition to fostering musical literacy, 'Rhythm Grids' and 'Play By Ear' lines provide early opportunities for composition and improvisation. This aspect of TEAM STRINGS can be a useful starting point for these elements in the GCSE examination course now followed by most secondary schools.

Comprehensive notes on the use of this series, scores of the ensemble material, piano accompaniments and approaches to creative music making are given in the ACCOMPANIMENTS book.

Supplementary Material

Parts are available for Brass, Woodwind, Recorder and Percussion which can be added to the TEAM STRINGS ensembles. Each piece can therefore be extended to incorporate a wide variety of additional instruments. These supplementary parts can be used for almost any combination of instruments from a small 'ad hoc' group to full orchestra.

Wind, Brass, and Percussion parts for the Ensemble Pieces in TEAM STRINGS are available separately.

Lesson diary & practice chart

Date (week commencing)	Enter number of minutes practised.							Teacher indicates which pages to study.
	Mon	Tue	Wed	Thur	Fri	Sat	Sun	
Date (week commencing)								Teacher indicates which pages to study.

. . . then on to A

D and A together

By the Rhine

This piece fits with *German tune* (page 23).

The note G

Music for the cello uses
the BASS CLEF

Open G
is written
on the
bottom
line

G and D together

A little march

Chiming bells

G, D and A

On the Lake

This piece fits with *Flamingo* (page 12).

The DOUBLE BAR marks the end of a piece of music

The traveller

This piece fits with *Tramping* (page 11).

The pendulum

This piece fits with *The clock* (page 15).

At dusk

This piece fits with *Now the day is over* (page 19).

Magic spells

This piece fits with *The wizard* (page 43).

Down bow

Using the bow

Up bow

ARCO means play with the bow.

PIZZICATO (or *pizz*) means pluck the strings.

From now on everything can be played *arco*, unless marked otherwise.

The bow hold

Use less bow for crotchets

Bowing exercises

Watch out for these signs

Always keep your bow straight!

■ The music on pages 2 - 7 can also be used as bowing exercises.

First finger E

This E is written in the third space

By the stream

The night sky

This piece fits with *Twinkle, twinkle little star* (page 27).

Third finger F♯

This F sharp is written on the fourth line

Tramping

Down bow

Traditional

The sharp sign, makes all the notes in the bar with the same letter name sharp

The shepherd

Bavaria

This piece fits with *German tune* (page 23).

Fourth finger G

This G is written in the top space

Flamingo

The magic carpet

This piece fits with *The wizard* (page 43).

Tunes using D E F♯ & G

A SEMIBREVE (or WHOLE NOTE) lasts for FOUR beats

The piper

Lucy

Folk song

Falling leaves

This piece fits with *Autumn* (page 21).

Notes on the G string

Merrily we roll along Traditional

On parade

The clock

In the belfry

Pennyroyal

Chorale

Scottish air

Rutland

The grasshopper

Notes on the A string

The harvest

Au clair de la lune

French traditional

Make up your own piece using the notes on the A string

Dance

The key signature of G   # The key signature of D

The sharp on the fourth line makes all the F's sharp

Promenade

The sharp in the second space make all the C's sharp

Daydreams

Five-note patterns

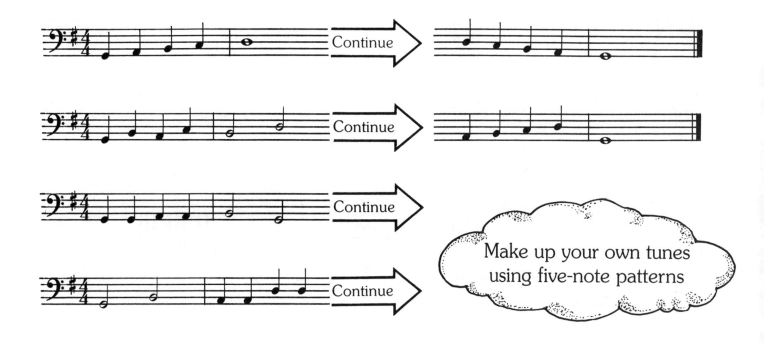

Make up your own tunes using five-note patterns

Now the day is over

S. BARING-GOULD (1834-1924)

Quick march

Mr Foster's round

Chinese lantern

Poor Tom

Duet

play by ear

Autumn

Dotted minims

A DOTTED MINIM
lasts for THREE beats

Count: 1   2   3

Sorrow

Rigaudon

HENRY PURCELL (1658-1695)

Arpeggios

Shady grove

American traditional

German tune

Traditional

Quavers

My goose

Round

Who's that yonder?

Spiritual

Procession

This old man

English traditional

Round go the mill wheels

French traditional

Song and dance

West Indian traditional

One player only

Everyone together

Popular song

American traditional

Start this piece on the FOURTH beat - count 1-2-3 then play

Twinkle, twinkle little star

Traditional

'Swops'

Duet

Play by ear

Little donkey

Words and Music by
ERIC BOSWELL

Okushiri

Japanese traditional

In $\frac{2}{4}$ time
each bar adds up
to TWO beats

Kol dodi

Jewish traditional

Russian lullaby

Go tell Aunt Rhody

American traditional

Magnolia

Long, long ago

T. H. BAYLY

29

Composing your own music

Round

Workin' on the railroad

Notes on the C string

Cowboy song

Ozibani

Tribal song from Zambia

Welcome spring

Swiss traditional

Hide and seek

German traditional

3/4 time

Each bar adds up to three crotchet beats

Waltz

Going home

Fine means 'the end'

Go back to the beginning and finish at the bar marked *Fine*

Blow the wind southerly

English traditional

Chanson

Eliza

Go back to the sign 𝄋 and play through to the word *Fine*

Past three o'clock

English traditional carol

Fine

D.C. al Fine

Oranges and lemons

English traditional

London's burning

Round

English traditional

(1)   (2)   (3)   (4)

Ye banks and braes

Scottish traditional

A handsome lad

Irish traditional

Congratulations

Words and Music by
BILL MARTIN and PHIL COULTER

Minuet

WOLFGANG AMADEUS MOZART
(1756-1791)

Mongoose

Brightly

Jamaican traditional

The prospector

Up bow

Steadily

American traditional

Schottisch

FRANZ SCHUBERT
(1797-1828)

Simply

Now we are met

Slowly

Duet

Dotted crotchets

Clap, say, and play the rhythm

Michael row the boat ashore

Spiritual

Moderately

The muffin man

English traditional

Rhythmically

Village song

Peruvian traditional

Not too fast

THREE MINIM BEATS in each bar

Kum ba yah

Spiritual

Edelweiss

From *The Sound of Music*

Lyrics by OSCAR HAMMERSTEIN II
Music by RICHARD RODGERS

London bridge

English traditional

Donkey riding

Traditional

Music for viols

Paloma blanca

Slurs

The notes joined by a SLUR are played in one bow

Separate bows

Slur

Scale of G

Etude

Ode to joy

From the *Ninth Symphony*

LUDWIG VAN BEETHOVEN
(1770-1827)

Majestically

The wizard

1st and 2nd-time bars

The nightingale

On the repeat, omit these bars and go straight to the bar marked |2

Bonjour!

Composed by twelve-year old Bernadette Walker

Allegro

TIELMAN SUSATO (c.16th)

Jingle bells

Presto

American traditional

The first Nowell

Joyfully

English traditional carol

O come, all ye faithful

Moderato   (Accompaniment)

J. F. WADE (1711-1786)

O little town of Bethlehem

Moderato   (Accompaniment)

English traditional carol

Tied notes

Clap, say, and play the rhythm

A minim tied to a crotchet lasts for 3 beats

A crotchet tied to a crotchet lasts for 2 beats

A semibreve tied to a crotchet lasts for 5 beats, and so on

When the saints go marching in

Up bow

American traditional

Old Texas

Up bow

American traditional

Syncopation

> Clap, say, and play the rhythm

The rolling heather

Scottish traditional

Twelve bar blues

Jamaican dance

Traditional

All night, all day

Spiritual

The clowns

I gave my love a cherry

Passion chorale

Old Macdonald

Traditional

The key of G major

Love me tender

Words and Music by
VERA MATSON and ELVIS PRESLEY

Valse

Yankee Doodle

American traditional

The grand old Duke of York

English traditional

Summer song

Czech traditional

Lullaby

O come, all ye faithful

J.F. WADE (1711-1786)

play by ear

Good King Wenceslas

English traditional carol

1.

2.

3.

$\frac{6}{8}$ **Time**

and its relationship with $\frac{2}{4}$ time.

Semiquavers

Four SEMIQUAVERS (or SIXTEENTH NOTES) add up to one crotchet

Clap, say, and play the rhythm

Semiquaver study

Allegro

Gallop

JACQUES OFFENBACH (1819-1880)

From the opera *Orpheus in the Underworld*

Allegro vivo

Dotted quavers

Clap, say, and play the rhythm

Happy birthday to you

Words and Music by
PATTY S. HILL and MILDRED HILL

Oh Susannah

American traditional

TWO MINIM BEATS in each bar

Chitty chitty bang bang

Words and Music by
RICHARD SHERMAN and ROBERT SHERMAN

Scarboro' fair

Traditional

The QUAVER TRIPLET means that three quavers are played in the time of one crotchet

Amazing grace

Traditional

2nd finger

Slurring three notes to a bow

Ruthin gardens

Tyrolean song

Silent night

FRANZ GRUBER
(1787-1863)

The Skye boat song

Scottish traditional

> RIT. (ritardando) means 'slowing down'

Scales and arpeggios

G Major

D Major

C Major

C Major (2 octaves)